ACCENT
UK

ZOMBIES

Edited by
**DAVE WEST &
COLIN MATHIESON**

Cover/endpapers art by
STEVE BISSETTE

Contents/back cover art by
SHANE OAKLEY

Book design by
ANDY BLOOR

WWW.ACCENTUKCOMICS.COM

ZOMBIES Volume 1. Published by Accent UK Comics 2007. All stories and artwork are the property and Copyright © of the creators involved and not Accent UK. All rights reserved. Reproduction of any of this book is strictly prohibited unless prior permission is given by either Accent UK of the creators, except for review purposes when no more than one page of any strip can be used. Published by Accent UK, 8 Stelfox Avenue, Timperley, Cheshire WA15 6UL. **ISBN 978-0-9555764-0-9** Printed in the UK by UKCOMICS CREATIVE **www.ukcomicscreative.co.uk** Second printing 2015.

CONTENTS

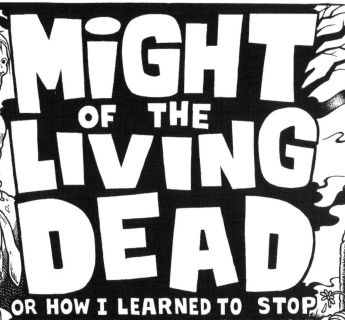

"An Molethy a an Ny-marow"
(The Curse of the Un-dead)

Story - Leah Moore
& John Reppion.
Art - David Hitchcock.

Gilling, Cornwall, 1859.

There be the Sergeant!

"It 'ad been a gloriously sunny day. We'd 'ave been sat idle, drinking scrumpy somewhere 'ad it not been for Sam and Jack vanishin' off."

Oh Sergeant, tell me you've found 'em!

Please!

I'm afraid not Missus Paynter.

But there's no sense in searchin' in the dark.

I'll take a party out at first light.

We'll find the boys soon, I'm sure of it.

We're going to have one in the Gardener's afore we turn in. Will you join us Jack?

I'll not, but, if young Seth's in there, tell him I said to get home.

We've all got another long day ahead of us.

Memories

STORY BY TONY HITCHMAN
ART BY LEONIE O'MOORE

LISTEN! LISTEN YOU CAN HEAR THEM IN THE STILLNESS OF THE NIGHT, THE DRUMS, THE NATIVE DRUMS. REMEMBER HOW THEY USED TO FRIGHTEN YOU?

IT SEEMS SO LONG AGO. WE WERE SO YOUNG THEN WHEN WE FIRST CAME TO THE ISLAND. IT ALL SEEMED SO STRANGE, SO FRIGHTENING THEN. THE NATIVES, THE DRUMS, THE RITUALS WERE FROM ANOTHER AGE AND WE WERE THE INTERLOPERS. WE THOUGHT WE WOULD NEVER STAY.

YET HERE WE ARE. WE WENT AMONG THE NATIVE, LEARNT THEIR WAYS. WE LEARNED TO ACCEPT, TO ADAPT, NOW WE COULD NEVER BE ANYWHERE ELSE.

WE HAVE A PLACE HERE.
TOGETHER.
JUST AS WE WERE ALL
THOSE YEARS AGO.

SPIRIT OF THE APOCALYPSE

by Benjamin Dickson

MORNING, TONY!

OH! MORNING JOHN. ROUGH NIGHT, WAS IT?

YEAH, PRETTY ROUGH. WHOLE LOAD OF 'EM BROKE THROUGH OUR LINE AND GOT INTO THE AREA. GOT PRETTY MESSY. SORTED 'EM ALL OUT THOUGH, WE'RE JUST MOPPING UP NOW.

ONE OF THE BASTARDS GOT ME TOO, SEE?

STILL, IT'S NOT DEEP.

JEEZ! WELL LET'S HOPE YOU'RE NOT INFECTED, EH?

YEAH, LET'S HOPE!

SEE YOU LATER!

TEN LAMBERT AND BUTLER AS WELL PLEASE, BAKARI.

COMING UP, MY FRIEND!

PARIAH.

VOCALS : JON AYRE
VISUALS : ONE NECK

IT'S LONELY ON THE STREETS.

IT'S BAD AT NIGHT, BUT IT'S WORSE IN THE DAYLIGHT.

THEY WON'T COME NEAR ME.

THEY CROSS THE STREET TO AVOID ME.

THEY THINK I'M SUBHUMAN,

I WAS NORMAL ONCE - I HAD A FAMILY - A WIFE AND SON,

AND I LOVED THEM SO MUCH.

BUT I HAVE FEELINGS AND IT HURTS. IT REALLY HURTS.

BUT THEN IT ALL CHANGED.

IT STARTED SO SMALL.

SO INNOCUOUS.

YOU PROBABLY REMEMBER IT.

JUST A FEW VOLUNTEERS.

AND AN EXPIREMENTAL DRUG.

JUST A FEW STEM CELLS TO BOOST THE IMMUNE SYSTEM.

BUT THEN IT ALL WENT WRONG.

FOR A WHILE IT WAS TOUCH AND GO.

I REMEMBER WATCHING THE NEWS AND THINKING 'POOR SODS - THEY HAVEN'T GOT A CHANCE'.

BUT THEY DID.

THE MEDIA FRENZY LASTED FOR A FEW DAYS BEFORE THE NEXT SENSATION STOLE OUR ATTENTION AWAY,

IF ONLY THE VOLUNTEERS HAD BEEN SO LUCKY.

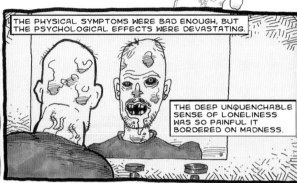

THE PHYSICAL SYMPTOMS WERE BAD ENOUGH, BUT THE PSYCHOLOGICAL EFFECTS WERE DEVASTATING.

THE DEEP UNQUENCHABLE SENSE OF LONELINESS WAS SO PAINFUL IT BORDERED ON MADNESS.

BUT WHO WOULD GO NEAR SOMEONE WHO LOOKED AND SMELLED LIKE A WALKING CORPSE ?

ESPECIALLY WHEN IT BECAME CLEAR THAT THE DISEASE WAS CONTAGIOUS.

THE GOVERNMENT WAS SLOW TO ACT.

BUT WHEN THEY DID,

IT WAS DECISIVE, EXCESSIVE AND MERCILESS.

DO NOT FEED! KEEP OUT!

THEY TREATED US LIKE CATTLE, HEALTHY OR INFECTED, AND CALLED IT 'CONTAINMENT'.

BUT HOW DO YOU CONTAIN THE UNDEAD ?

HOW DO YOU STOP SOMETHING THAT JUST KEEPS GETTING UP AGAIN NO MATTER HOW MANY TIMES YOU SHOOT IT ?

The Zombie Interviews

Subject: Augst Simplefather

Date and time: Inanna, After breaking fast

Interview conducted by David Baillie

C'MON SHANNON, I HATE SHOPPING AS MUCH AS YOU DO.

WHY DIDN'T WE GO ON THE MARCH AGAIN, MUM?

LIVE

STORY PHIL RIGBY

Z

ART MANOEL MAGALHAES

BECAUSE YOU NEED SHOES, SHANNON. YOU'RE BACK AT SCHOOL ON MONDAY.

I HATE SCHOOL.

I HATE PEOPLE WHO ASSOCIATE READING *THE GUARDIAN* WITH MAKING A DIFFERENCE.

AND THINK MARCHING FROM HERE TO THERE...

...DOES ANYTHING TO CHANGE THIS CRAPPY WORLD.

LIKE CRAPPY SCHOOL?

TLIM!

HA! HA! YES, LOVE. LIKE CRAPPY SCHOOL.

The SLOW UNDEATH.

by
Dave West.

1986. SOMETIME.

IF I TRY REAL HARD, I CAN STILL REMEMBER MY FIRST DAY HERE.

THERE WERE THREE OF US.

LIZ, DAVE AND ME.

FRESH FROM UNIVERSITY.

NO. I THINK THERE WERE OTHERS TOO.

I JUST CAN'T QUITE PICTURE THEM.

WE WERE GOING TO MAKE A REAL IMPRESSION.

MAKE A DIFFERENCE.

DO WELL.

AND WHY NOT?

15:13

ALL AROUND US THE PEOPLE SEEMED SO SLOW.

SLOW AND TIRED.

THEY WEREN'T LIKE US.

NO.

NOT LIKE US AT ALL.

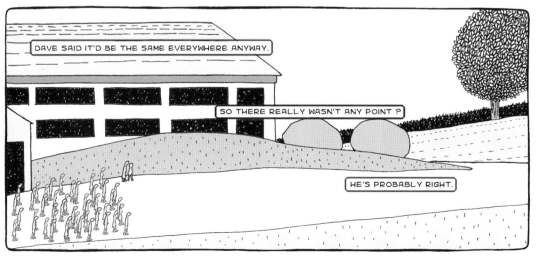

Zombie thespian ~ on the set of "undead face munch Part 7" by Matt Boyce

I did'nt always Portray Zombies In cheap movies

I was one of the finest Shakespearean actors of my generation, I played hamlet all over the world to great Critical acclaim

I SANG on stage at broadway

I even starred in my own short lived t.v. series where I Portrayed a stamp collecting-ninja-Private detective

COME ON, YOU TWO. TO BED WITH YOU.

"ONE"

DARREN ELLIS WRITER
ROLAND BIRD ARTIST
PABLO LIZALDE LETTERER

BUT DAD, I'VE NEVER GOT PAST THIS BIT!

JUST SAVE YOUR GAME, SWEETIE. YOUR DAD'S TIRED AND HE NEEDS TO TURN IN.

MUUUUUUM!

YOU HEARD YOUR DAD. HE'S ON EARLIES THIS WEEK, SO HE'LL BE UP REALLY EARLY.

TELL YOU WHAT, SOPHIE. YOU BE GOOD THIS WEEK AND WE'LL GO TO THE ZOO ON SATURDAY AND SEE THE LIONS.

AND THE PENGUINS? CAN WE GO SEE THE PENGUINS TOO?

OF COURSE WE CAN, BARB.

YAY PENGUINS!

COME ON, SOPH. GO CLEAN YOUR TEETH. I'LL TUCK YOU IN ONCE I'VE GOT BARB SETTLED DOWN.

I DON'T NEED TUCKING IN, DAD, I'M NEARLY *EIGHT*.

THAT JUST MEANS IT TAKES ME A BIT LONGER.

WE REALLY GOING TO THE ZOO ON SATURDAY, DADDY?

COURSE WE ARE, PICKLE. IF YOUR DADDY SAYS WE'RE DOING SOMETHING, THAT MEANS WE DO IT.

BUT WHAT WILL WE DO WHEN WE GO OUT?

WE'LL BE CAREFUL, 'CAUSE THE BAD PEOPLE MIGHT BE ANYWHERE.

THAT'S MY GIRL. G'NIGHT, BARB.

YOU NOT GONNA READ ME THE TWITS AGAIN?

MAYBE TOMORROW. NIGHT, SWEETIE.

NIGHT, DADDY.

I GUESS I SHOULDN'T HAVE LIED TO THEM, BUT I'D BE PUTTING THEM IN DANGER IF I DIDN'T.

WHO KNOWS WHO WOULD WAKE UP NEXT TO ELISA TOMORROW?

AND I WON'T LOCK THEM INSIDE THE HOUSE WITH A MONSTER.

I OWE THEM BETTER THAN THAT. I OWE THEM THEIR *SURVIVAL*.

IT'S FUNNY HOW ONE TINY LITTLE THING CAN ALTER PLANS. SHIFT INTENTIONS. CHANGE YOUR WORLD. *THEIR* WORLD.

ONE BITE.

ONE GESTURE.

ONE GIFT.

DFF

FOR *THEM*.

END.

The Zombie Interviews

Subject: Figg Duggastoll (and Toto)

Date and time: Utu, Almost dusk

Interview conducted by David Baillie

Tom the TOM

ARTWORK & SCRIPT
BY JAMES GRAY

TOM WAS AN ORDINARY
SORT OF CHILD

HE LIKED THE USUAL KIND OF THINGS THAT 10 YEAR OLD BOYS ENJOYED TO DO. KICKING A BALL ABOUT QUEENS PARK WITH HIS FRIENDS, SWIMMING, VIDEO GAMES, PLAYING WITH WORMS IN THE GARDEN THEN LEAVING THEM ON THE KITCHEN TABLE FOR HIS MUM TO FIND WHEN SHE'D FINISHED THE IRONING.

THAT ALL CHANGED ON 27TH FEBRUARY 2008.

IT WAS A WEDNESDAY AFTERNOON, AND TOM HAD JUST COME HOME FROM SCHOOL. HIS DAD WAS WORKING, AS USUAL, IN HIS OFFICE UPSTAIRS AND MUM WAS JUST FINISHING OFF ANOTHER MOUNTAIN OF CLOTHES. SHE LOOKED UP AS TOM ENTERED AND...

... THAT'S ALL TOM REMEMBERS.

THE 2012 UNDEAD DISCRIMINATION ACT STATES THAT ALL UDEAD CHILDREN ARE ENTITLED TO A PLACE IN REGULAR STATE AND PRIVATE SCHOOLS. SINCE LATE 2010 CHILDREN, AND ONLY CHILDREN, HAVE BEEN COMING BACK FROM THE DEAD. THE SPATE OF BOMBINGS EARLIER THAT YEAR DECIMATED THE POPULATION OF SOUTHERN ENGLAND. NO ONE KNOWS WHO WAS RESPONSIBLE, BUT THE TOP KNOBS IN GOVERNMENT HAVE TOLD THE POPULACE THAT IT IS DUE TO THE RADIOACTIVE NATURE OF THE DEVICES THAT IS SOMEHOW REANIMATING THE DEAD.

BECAUSE ONLY CHILDREN ARE BEING BROUGHT BACK FROM THE DEAD, THIS IS, OF COURSE, GIVING RISE TO A LARGE NUMBER OF *"ORPHANED ZOMBIES"*.

The Zombie Interviews

Subject: Kwott Scarabeater

Date and time: Enlil, Noon

Interview conducted by David Baillie

The Scent of Coriander

by Andrew Cheverton
& Tim Keable.

'Bye, babe. I'll be back soon.

Hey, Gary. And how are you today?

Fine, Mr. Day. Yourself?

Very well, thank you.

Tom Land wanted to talk to you - he has some supplies to trade.

I'll try to see him later in the week. I'm going to be busy today.

Okay, son. You be careful out there.

WINCHESTER
STREET
W.3

Happy anniversary, Dawn.

Oh. Are we... going out tonight, then?

No, babe.

Not tonight, not if you don't want to.

No, I don't want to go out.

DISSOLUTION

There came a day
when Rabbit asked
a question
Mr Maximo
couldn't answer...

*Words and pictures
by
Bridgeen Gillespie*

b.gillespie (c) 2007

b.gillespie (c) 2007

b.gillespie 2007

FIN.

STOP!! WHAT THE HELL DO YOU THINK YOU'RE *DOING??*

THAT'S WHAT WE'RE FIGHTING! THE HOARDS OF THE UNDEAD, NOT EACH OTHER! REMEMBER??

I'M SORRY, BABE! YOU KNOW YOU'RE MY BEST FRIEND, YEAH?

OH, WE ARE *SO* GOING ON THE BIGGEST GIRLY SHOP EVER WHEN WE GET OUT OF HERE!

THAT'S RIGHT, GIRLS – NICE AND FRIENDLY. HEEHHH...

SEE, THIS IS WHY I'M THE SURLY LONER TYPE.

...

>SIGH< WE NEVER USED TO FIGHT WHEN BARNABY WAS ALIVE.

POOR BASTARD.

YEAH, HE COULD ALWAYS LIGHTEN THE MOOD WITH HIS PRACTICAL JOKES AND KNOB GAGS.

HE WAS A *TOSSER,* SAME AS THE REST OF YEZ!

end.

The Zombie Interviews

Subject: Thur Transelgansst

Date and time: Nanna, After Noon

Interview conducted by David Baillie

THE SWEETEST OF DREAMS

STORY AND ART BY B.C. STERRETT

Once while cleaning out my closet, I found an old severed head.

I put it on the shelf, just for decoration.

One night while staring at it in quiet meditation I had a revelation!

Voices began to chant as if from some distant forgotten past.

THE HEAD IS ALIVE
KEEP IT ALIVE
THE HEAD IS ALIVE
KEEP IT A...

Feed it casserole, Feed it casserole, Feed it casserole!!!

The Zombie Interviews

Subject: Wynn Jamalandin

Date and time: Enki, Before noon

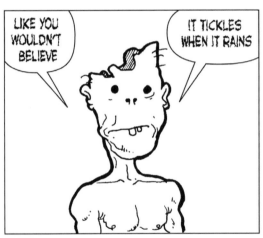

Interview conducted by David Baillie

DR CALIMARI CREATED BY ARTHUR CULLIPHER

By DENIS St. JOHN & JACI JUNE

AND SO IT BEGAN, A GENUINE ROMANCE...

IT STARTED AS A DESIRE TO PROTECT, AND THEN IT MOVED ONTO RESPECT.

AND IT ENDED IN AN UNCONDITIONAL LOVE.

I KNOW YOU LOVE ME! IF YOU DIDN'T THIS WOULDN'T WORK!

W-WHA AAAA!

HAHAHA! WITH YOUR LOVE I CAN CONTINUE TO LIVE & BE BEAUTIFUL ONCE MORE! YOU SEE, I'M NO INNOCENT TEENAGE GIRL—BUT A HEART EATING DEMON FROM HELL! FAREWELL, JIM!

GURGLE...

SPURRT!

SO WHAT CAN JIMMY DO? HE'S STILL ALIVE, BUT HE'S EMPTY INSIDE. HE'S LIVING—YET DEAD...

SO HE WAITS, BUT FOR WHO KNOWS WHAT? IS THIS WHAT A MAN WITHOUT LOVE IS LIKE? A ZOMBIE?

BUT AS THEY SAY... ONCE LOVED IS NEVER FORGOTTEN...

YOU!!

DR CALIMARI CREATED BY ARTHOR CULLIPHER

The Zombie Interviews

Subject: Singsta

Date and time: Gugalaana, Around Noon

Interview conducted by David Baillie

"ZOMBIES"

WRITER: KIERON GILLEN
ARTIST: ANDY BLOOR

I USED TO KNOW HOW LONG
THIS HAD BEEN GOING ON.

I USED TO COUNT
THE DAYS.

I DON'T ANYMORE.

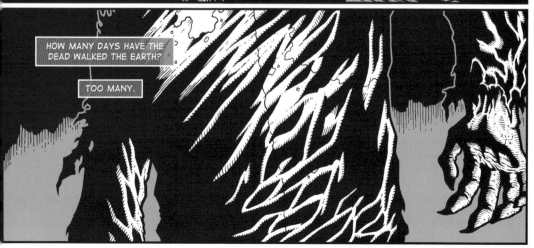

HOW MANY DAYS HAVE THE
DEAD WALKED THE EARTH?

TOO MANY.

BUT I'M STILL ALIVE.

HOW DO YOU SURVIVE IN A WORLD FULL OF MONSTERS?

YOU PRETEND.

THEY'RE NOT SMART.

IF YOU ACT LIKE ONE...

YOU ARE ONE.

IF YOU CAN PRETEND YOU'RE NOT ALIVE.

THEN YOU CAN BE.

SO YOU WALK LIKE YOU WERE BROKEN AT THE ANKLE.

AND YOU DROOL.

LET YOUR CLOTHES FALL APART.

YOU SMEAR YOURSELF IN... EVERYTHING.

EVERY-FUCKING-THING.

YOU BUMP INTO DOORS.

UHHH.

WITHOUT SAYING "OW".

I STILL CLEAN MY TEETH.

CAN'T HELP IT.

BUT BEFORE I SHAMBLE OUT, I PREPARE MYSELF.

EVERY DAY, ALL I CAN TASTE IS OLD MEAT.

I'M NOT SURE WHETHER I'M MORE SCARED OF RUNNING OUT OF FOOD...

OR RUNNING OUT OF TOOTHPASTE.

THE END OF THE WORLD HAS TAUGHT ME TWO THINGS:

1. WHAT SOMEONE CAN DO TO STAY ALIVE.

2. THAT CIVILIZATION COMES IN A SQUEEZABLE TUBE WITH A NOZZLE.

JUST WAIT IT OUT. IT CAN'T LAST FOREVER.

YOU SEE ONE OF THEM JUST... SLUMP. WHATEVER KEEPS THEM GOING JUST WEARING OUT.

IT'S A QUESTION OF PERSISTENCE. A QUESTION OF...

OH NO!

GET THE FUCK AWAY FROM ME.

OH NO.

THE WORST BIT.

THE SWEETEST OF DREAMS
STORY AND ART BY B.C. STERRETT

Once, I worked in a lab where we taught ourselves how to create new life!

We would fill capsules with living organic liquid...

and mold our own humans, like instant waffles—

actual people who could act & think for themselves.

They only had the intelligence of dogs & cats, so we gave them names like Fido & Fluffy.

Pant Pant Pant Pant

One day, residue from the capsules collected and made its own human!

It scared me to DEATH!

CRASH

Unfortunately, I had taught it to throw things.

He was really quite pleasant & would often go with us for walkies.

Till the day he wandered off & we never saw him again.

TO OPEN

Missing MiLK 1% lowfat vitamins A & D

Last Seen 11/6/03

Lap Lap Lap

BC Sterrett 11/03

ORION STAR

by MORGAN PIELLI

"LAST WEEK'S **ORION STAR** HIJACKING, THE WORST TERROR ATTACK IN NEARLY A DECADE, IS NOW BEING LINKED TO THE BRUTAL STRING OF MAULINGS THAT CONTINUE TO SPREAD THROUGHOUT THE NORTH-EAST."

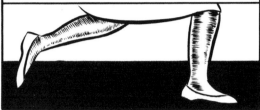

"THESE GUYS CAME OUT OF NO-WHERE; GRABBING AND BITING... KILLING PEOPLE WITH THEIR **BARE HANDS**!"

"THERE DOESN'T APPEAR TO BE ANY MOTIVE BEHIND THE ATTACKS. WE CAN ONLY ASSUME THAT THE INTENTION IS TO SPREAD FEAR."

"RESPONDING TO THE CRISIS, CONGRESS HAS DRAFTED A BILL THAT WILL GRANT LAW ENFORCEMENT GREATER LATITUDE IN FIGHTING TERROR."

"WHERE ARE ALL THESE TERRORISTS COMING FROM? THEY CAN'T **ALL** BE FROM THE ORION STAR."

"I SAW PEOPLE AMOUNG THE TERRORISTS I THOUGHT HAD BEEN KILLED! THEY WERE PALE, LIKE THE TERRORISTS, AND THEY LOOKED LIKE THEY HAD BEEN BITTEN!"

"THE NATIONAL INSTITUTE OF HEALTH ANNOUNCED TODAY THAT THEY HAVE DEVELOPED AN INOCULATION DESIGNED TO COUNTER-ACT TERRORIST BRAINWASHING."

"DRUGGING THE POPULACE MAY SEEM DRASTIC, BUT THESE ARE DRASTIC TIMES."

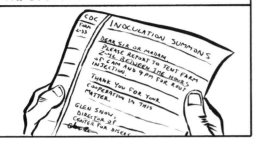

"I'M HERE NOW WITH ONE OF THE VERY FIRST VOLUNTEERS TO RECEIVE THE INOCULATION. HOW DO YOU FEEL, MR. STULTZ?"

"I FEEL FINE, TOM! JUST A BIT GROGGY. ABOUT THE ONLY SCARY PART WAS SEEING THE NEEDLE!"

"HA, HA. INDEED. AND WHAT ABOUT THAT REDNESS ALL DOWN YOUR ARM?"

"...WHAT REDNESS?"

"THERE, ON YOUR ARM - ER.. ARE YOU ALRIGHT MR. STULTZ? YOU LOOK RATHER **PALE**.."

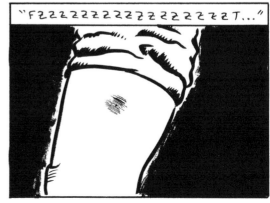

"..MR. STULTZ? .. UM, MR. ST—"

"GAH! JESUS CHRIST! GET HIM OFF OF ME! HE'S B-**GLURG**—..."

"FZZZZZZZZZZZZZZZZZZZT..."

NO TIME TO DIE

STORY :-
CHRIS DINGSDALE.

ART :-
DAN DENHOLT.

" THE MOST IMPORTANT EVENTS IN
OUR LIVES HAPPEN IN BARS.
THAT'S A STATEMENT NOT A QUESTION.
THINK ABOUT IT.
FINISHED?
YOU KNOW I'M RIGHT. "

" FOR EXAMPLE; IT'S LATE SATURDAY
NIGHT. I'M BORED, IRRITABLE AND
ALONE. ANY THOUGHTS OF LEAVING
VANISH WHEN I GLACE UP AND NOTICE
THE 2 WANNABE GODDESSES. SOME
LAME CHAT UP LINE ABOUT 'LOOKING
AFTER A FRIEND UNTIL SOMEONE ELSE
TURNS UP' SECURES MY INTEREST. "

" BLOKES, 50% EGO.
50% BULLSHIT.
AGAIN IT'S NOT A
QUESTION.
AT THE TIME I
ACTUALLY BELIEVED
THAT THEY WERE
INTERESTED IN ME.
THE ALCOHOL
FUELLING MY
EXPECTATION OF
WHERE THIS WAS
GOING TO END UP. "

" MET MY GIRLFRIEND LATER ON.
SEX TURNED INTO AN ORDEAL
WHEN I FELT SOMETHING SNAP.
SHE SEEMED UPSET.
A BIT UNREASONABLE I THOUGHT.
SO I LEFT.
5 INCHES SHORTER (BUT STILL AS
TALL). "

" I STILL WASN'T THINKING STRAIGHT
BUT A HASTY RETREAT TO THE
FAMILY SUMMER COTTAGE
SEEMED WISE.
THE THOUGHT OF ALL THAT
WILDLIFE NEARBY STARTED TO
APPEAL.
I COULD PRACTICALLY TASTE IT. "

" IN BETWEEN MEALS
I WATCHED TV.
SLOWLY THE PROGRAMS
WERE REPLACED BY
NEWS, NEWS, NEWS.
YOU WOULD HAVE
THOUGHT THE WORLD
WAS ENDING. "

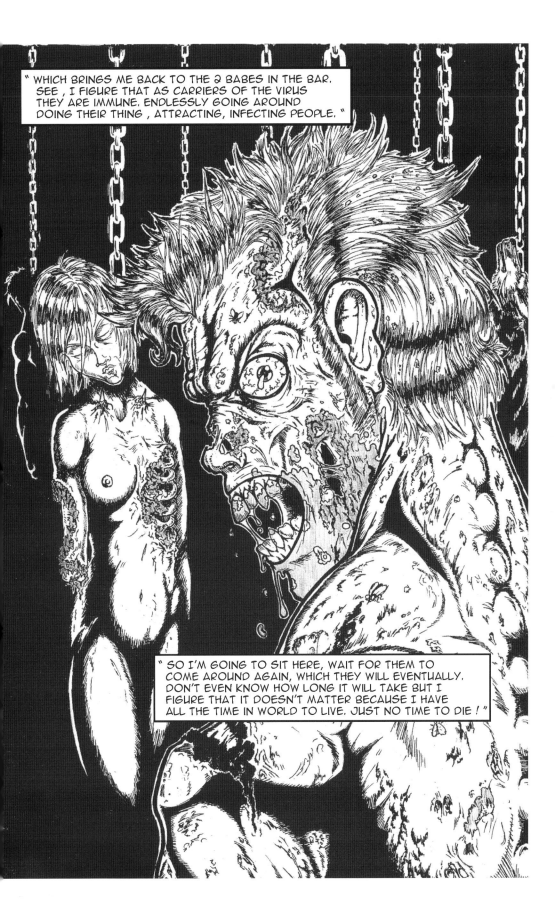

" WHICH BRINGS ME BACK TO THE 2 BABES IN THE BAR.
SEE , I FIGURE THAT AS CARRIERS OF THE VIRUS
THEY ARE IMMUNE. ENDLESSLY GOING AROUND
DOING THEIR THING , ATTRACTING, INFECTING PEOPLE. "

" SO I'M GOING TO SIT HERE, WAIT FOR THEM TO
COME AROUND AGAIN, WHICH THEY WILL EVENTUALLY,
DON'T EVEN KNOW HOW LONG IT WILL TAKE BUT I
FIGURE THAT IT DOESN'T MATTER BECAUSE I HAVE
ALL THE TIME IN WORLD TO LIVE. JUST NO TIME TO DIE ! "

SOME HORROR STORIES HAVE A REAL STING IN THE TALE!

ATTACK OF THE ZOM-BEES

WATCH OUT...THEY'LL BEE COMING TO GET YOU!

Accent UK Comics Presents 'ATTACK OF THE ZOM-BEES' Created, Written and Illustrated by Andy Bloor

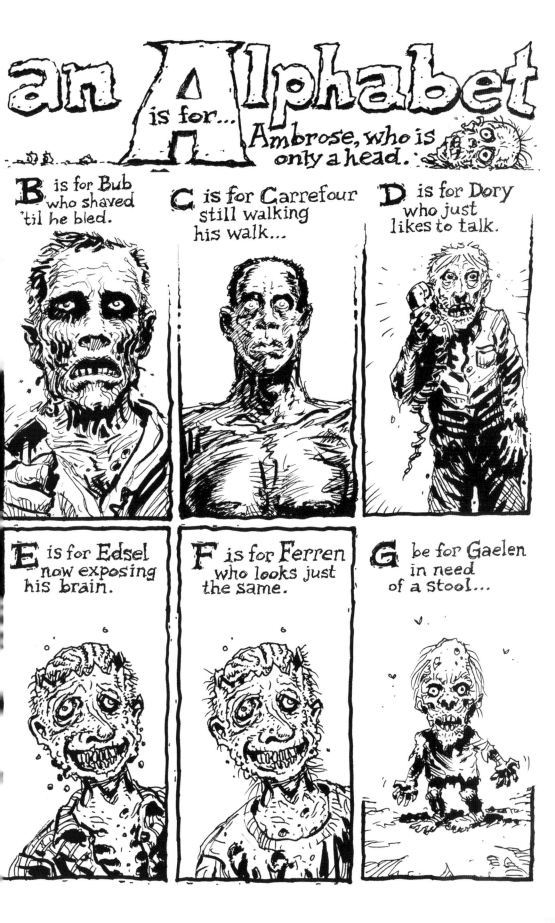

H brings in
Henrik the
trash-dancin' fool.

I is for Inez
who's fetching
and comely...

J is for Jésus,
he was nailed
by a Humvee.

K is for Karl
whose eyes
were sewn closed;

L is for Louie
who's holding
his nose.

M is Malachai
who stepped
in a trap.

N is for Nedley
whose ass
is a hat.

O is for Onio
adrift
in the sea...

P is for Paul
inching closer
to thee.

Q is for Quentin
who still thinks
he's funny...

R is for Regan
who's really
quite runny.

S is for Samuel
lurking outside
your house ~~

T brings Tierra chowing down on her spouse.

U finds Ulrich in the pit he was flung...

V is for Victor (he's still badly hung).

W is for Wendy her head's blown to shit...

X is for Xavier who just wants to sit.

Y is for Yusef who won't go to bed.

PICK SNIK

...of Zombies ...is for [____]ed and his buds (who are dead!)

© 2007 D Bissette & S Bissette (Thanx to Rache Johnson)

TRAGIC KINGDOM

Story : - Owen Johnson
Art : - Garry Brown

"Welcome to the Magic Kingdom,
Where happiness is found..."

" ... Children's laughter echoes
And smiles are all around ... "

"... See all the characters,
they can't wait to meet you..."

"...And take a snapshot,
To take home when you're through..."

" ... Inside the Magic Kingdom,
Is the happiness you seek ... "

" ... Nothing can hurt you ,
In the trees of Walnut Creek ... "

The Zombie Interviews

Subject: Ryomero Ryusso

Date and time: Ninurta, Noon

Interview conducted by David Baillie

The Zombie Interviews

Subject: David Baillie

Date and time: A moment ago

A LOT OF THE CONCEPTS WE ASSOCIATE WITH ZOMBIES IN FICTION ORIGINATED WITH THE 1968 HORROR CLASSIC *NIGHT OF THE LIVING DEAD*.

INCLUDING THE CONVENTION THAT THE CHARACTERS IN A ZOMBIE MOVIE SHOULDN'T USE THE WORD 'ZOMBIE'

WHICH IS PROBABLY DERIVED FROM 'ZOMBI' - ANOTHER NAME FOR THE VOODOO GOD *DAMBALLAH WEDO*

IT IS A UNIVERSALLY ACKNOWLEDGED TRUTH THAT THE VAST MAJORITY OF THE POPULATION SPEND A LARGE PART OF THE LIVES -

SLUMPED IN FRONT OF A TELEVISION OR COMPUTER SCREEN... MUCH LIKE A ZOMBIE.

ALTHOUGH, BY AND LARGE, THEIR BRAINS STAY IN WHEN THEY FART.

Interview conducted by David Baillie

For Adam Best Wishes [signature] 2015

OUR BOYS **DIDN'T** QUESTION **WHY** THEY WERE **INVADING** AN **INNOCENT** COUNTRY FAR AWAY.

OR WHY THEIR COMMANDER, LORD CHELMSFORD, TOOK **HALF** HIS FORCE **AWAY** FROM THE UNDEFENDED CAMP ON THE MORNING OF THE SURPRISE **ATTACK!**

NO WHEN THOSE ZULU HORDES SUDDENLY APPEARED, OUR BOYS STOOD **FIRM** AND FOUGHT BACK!

THEIR WELL DRILLED FIRING LINES SOON PRODUCED **VOLLEY** AFTER **DEVASTATING** VOLLEY!

WHICH **TORE** THROUGH THE RANKS OF THOSE **BRAVE BARE** CHESTED **WARRIORS**

AND **APART** FROM THE **ODD LUCKY SHOT**

OUR BOYS SUFFERED **FEW** CASUALTIES

TO **START** WITH ANYWAY!

SOON **EVEN** THOSE BRAVE ZULUS HAD TO **FALL BACK** AND SEEK OUT **COVER** WHERE THEY COULD

THEIR ATTACK FALTERED

AS THEY BECAME **PINNED DOWN**

THE **ONLY** QUESTION WAS WHETHER OUR BOYS WOULD **RUN OUT** OF **AMMUNITION** FIRST

OR ZULUS?

KRAK

THE WATCHING ZULU CHIEF KNEW THE ATTACK **WAS FINISHED** UNLESS SOMETHING **DRASTIC** COULD BE DONE

AND HIS **ISANGOMA**, DIVINER OF **SUPERNATURAL** PHENOMENA WAS SUMMONED

AND **DANCED** HIMSELF INTO A **FRENZY** UNTO THE BATTLEFIELD!

WITH ALL HIS CHANTING AND PRANCING ABOUT HE WAS AN **EASY TARGET!**

BUT SOMEHOW THE SHOTS ALL MISSED!

AND THEN...THEN IT HAPPENED!

THE SUN BLACKED OUT LIKE A DEAD MOON!!

AND SLOWLY

SURELY

THE DEAD BEGAN TO RISE!!

IMAGINE OUR BOYS THOUGHTS AS THE **ENEMY** THEY HAD **KILLED** LUMBERED TOWARDS THEM **AGAIN!**

AND THIS TIME, THEIR BULLETS **COULDN'T STOP THEM!** BUT **STILL** OUR BOYS STOOD THEIR GROUND!

KRAK

KRAK

AND DIED, LIKE BRAVE MEN DO!

OUR BOYS WERE SOON OVERPOWERED AND THEN.. ..THEN THE SLAUGHTER BEGAN!

SOME OF THE BRITISH DEAD HAD BEEN CAUGHT BY THE SPELL TOO, AND LURCHED ABOUT THE BATTLEFIELD!

UNABLE TO HELP THEIR FALLEN COMRADES, THEY COULD NOT WATCH THE MINDLESS MASSACRE!

AND SAT DOWN OUT OF THE WAY, TRYING TO UNDERSTAND THEIR SITUATION!

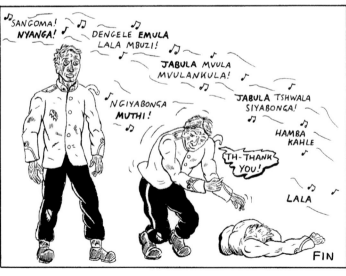

FIN

THE DESERT HAS NEVER BEEN A PLACE FOR THE LIVING.

BODIES DRY OUT. BECOME BRITTLE. TIGHT. IMMOBILE. A DAY OR TWO OUT HERE. AND THEY JUST SEIZE UP.

IT'S THE ONE ADVANTAGE WE HAVE OVER THE DEAD.

THE WORST PLACE IN THE WORLD TO LIVE. ONE OF THE FEW PLACES WE CAN SURVIVE.

ONCE WE WERE SOLDIERS. PARENTS. TEACHERS AND PREACHERS.

NOW WE'RE A TRIBE WANDERING THE DESERTS OF OUR CIVILISATION.

NOW. WE'RE SIMPLY...

NOMADS

STORY BY MARK CLAPHAM - ART AND LETTERS BY BJR

ONCE. THIS WOULD HAVE BEEN
A HAPPY. LIVING PLACE.

NOW FORMER OASES LIKE THESE ARE
GRAVEYARDS. WE ONLY ENTER THEM WHEN
WE HAVE TO.

FOOD. MEDICINE. WEAPONS.
LOST TREASURES FROM THE
FALLEN AGE OF MODERN MAN.

THIS IS WHERE THE DEAD WALK.

DRAWN TO WHATEVER MOISTURE THEY CAN FIND TO THE DARK PLACES.

OUR ROUTINE IS SIMPLE.

WHILE ONE GROUP KEEPS THEM AWAY. ANOTHER SWEEPS THE BUILDINGS FOR ANYTHING USEFUL.

YOU NEVER KNOW WHAT YOU CAN FIND.

SOMETIMES WE GET LUCKY.

FIN.

LOVE IS...

(after Marshall)

...never having to say goodbye.

2 HOURS AGO...

sacrifice

STORY – KIERAN BROWN   ART – NOLAN WORTHINGTON & SHAUN MOONEY

GIVE IT TO ME STRAIGHT, DOC...

...WHAT'S THE DAMAGE?

WHAT'S THE SITUATION!?

IT DOESN'T LOOK GOOD, KATE

HOW LONG DO I HAVE?

FIVE HOURS, MAYBE SIX...

...I CAN'T SAY FOR CERTAIN

I'M GOING BACK TO LOOK FOR SURVIVORS.

IT'S TOO DANGEROUS!

I'M A DEAD WOMAN WALKING, JAMES...

CLICK!

...NONE OF THAT MATTERS!

WHAT DOES MATTER IS THAT I MIGHT BE ABLE TO BRING SOMEONE BACK SAFELY FROM THAT HELLHOLE AND ACTUALLY GIVE MY DEATH MEANING

REVVVVVVV!

NOW...

'MY NAME IS KATE AUSTEN...'

CLICK!

'...AND THESE ARE THE FINAL HOURS OF MY LIFE.'

CLICK!

'I'M ALONE IN THIS CITY.'

'SEPARATED FROM THE REST OF THE GLOBAL DEFENSE INITIATIVE.'

CLACK!

'MY BIKE RAN OUT OF GAS AND I CAN'T FIND A WORKING VEHICLE OR SURVIVORS ANYWHERE.'

UUURRRGH?

'I'M ALONE...'

SNIFF!

'...AS GOOD AS DEAD.'

FLESSHHHH!!

A LITTLE FURTHER...

...JUST A LITTLE FURTHER.

COME ON, YOU LITTLE SHITS...

NO GUTS, NO GLORY.

BOOM!

SPLUTCH!

BOOM!

BOOM!

CLACK!

BOOM!

CLACK!

CLICK!

CLATTER!

BLAM!

BLAM!

CLICK!

CLICK!

'AND I'M ALSO OUT OF AMMO...'

CRACK!

'...THANK YOU VERY MUCH JESUS CHRIST.'

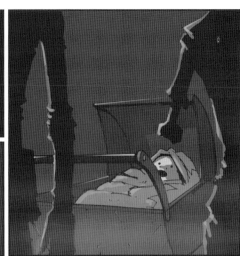

GRAB!

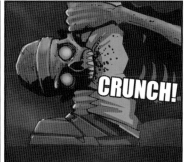

CRUNCH!

AAAAAARRGHH!!!

SONUVA...

...BITCH!

SPLUTCH!

'IT'S NOTHING, KATE, IT'S N..NOTHING ...YOU'RE A..ALREADY DEAD.'

'THE TURN TAKES AN AVERAGE OF SIX HOURS TO COMPLETE...'

'...IF I GET TO THE GDF BEFORE, THIS BABY BE SAFE...'

'...P..PERHAPS I GET THERE IN TIME...'

'...GET THE BABY, G..GET THE BABY.'

3 HOURS LATER...

'CLOZE, ME IFF CLOSSSE...KEE GOIN...'

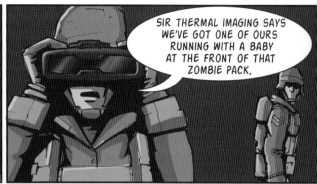

SIR THERMAL IMAGING SAYS WE'VE GOT ONE OF OURS RUNNING WITH A BABY AT THE FRONT OF THAT ZOMBIE PACK,

BIO READOUTS SUGGEST SHE'S TURNING THOUGH!

OPEN THE GATES AND GIVE THEM SOME COVERING FIRE.

ALL SOLDIERS TO DEFENSIVE BATTLE STATIONS!!

'ME...SURVIVE...MEEE MAKE IS...'

BUDDA! BUDDA! BUDDA! BUDDA!

FIRE!

BUDDA! BUDDA! BUDDA! BUDDA!

'YESSSSS...'

SLAM!

GOOOOD...

ME DOOO GOOOOD...

BENNNNNNNNN...

DO ITTT...

DOOOOO ITTTTT...

GOODBYE, KATE.

BLAM!

END.

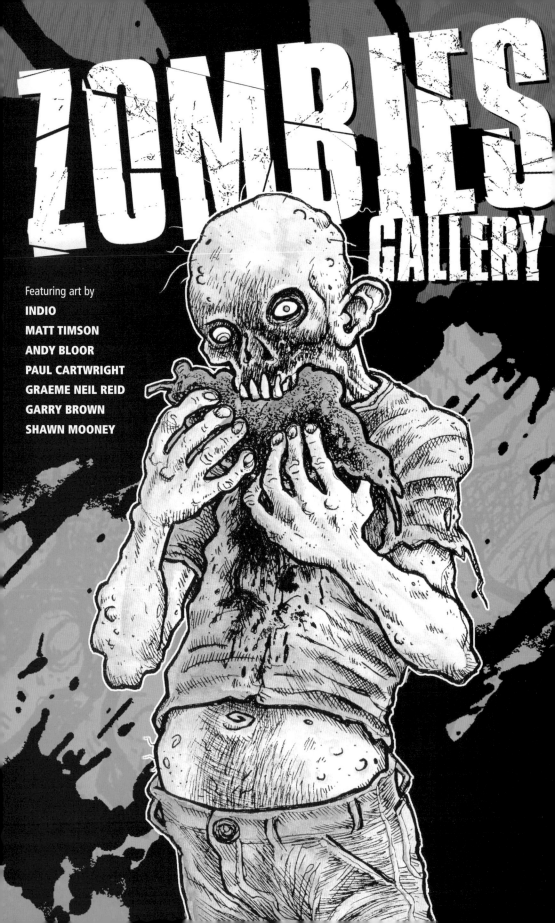

ZOMBIES
GALLERY

Featuring art by
INDIO
MATT TIMSON
ANDY BLOOR
PAUL CARTWRIGHT
GRAEME NEIL REID
GARRY BROWN
SHAWN MOONEY

ZOMBIE-COPS

You Have The Right To Remain... DEAD!